Number
Journey

for ages 5-6

A & C Black • London

Contents

Andrew Brodie: Number Journey for ages 5-6 © A&C Black Publishers Ltd 2008

Introduction

Number Journey has been specially written to help teachers ensure progression in the teaching of number by addressing two key areas: the involvement of parents and the use of day-to-day assessment to promote success.

For many parents, the current methods used for teaching mathematics can be something of a mystery. Parents recognise certain aspects from their own school days but are surprised by some of the other approaches that are now being used in schools. The clash between the methods with which the parents are familiar and the methods their children are using in school can lead to many frustrations at home. The Williams review of 'Mathematics Teaching in Early Years Settings and Primary Schools' emphasises the role that parents can play in helping their children to learn mathematics. This can be summarised in the following four statements:

- Parents should be at the centre of any plan to improve children's outcomes.

- The panel heard time and again from children that they would like their parents to be taught the methods they are learning in mathematics, which have changed considerably since their parents were at school.

- The panel believes that the lack of clarification and setting out of the methods of teaching is a missed opportunity for engaging parents and improving their children's attainment.

- There is an opportunity for schools to work together with parents to dispel myths about the mystery of mathematics and give both children and parents a good grounding and positive attitude to this subject.

Number Journey addresses all four statements by providing materials that schools can use to ensure parents are given the opportunity to take an active part in their children's mathematical education. Current methods are explained clearly and the explanations are accompanied by activities that can be used at home to provide positive support for work at school. The teachers' notes for each unit specify clear learning objectives and list both outcomes and success criteria to enable teachers to make reliable assessments of pupils' work. The worksheets themselves are used to determine whether pupils have met the success criteria.

Andrew Brodie: Number Journey for ages 5-6 © A&C Black Publishers Ltd 2008

How is the book organised?

The materials in this book are organised into 15 units all designed to address the teaching of number – an area of maths in which many parents feel least confident but where they can actually be most helpful. *The Framework for mathematics teaching* includes a very wide range of learning objectives for understanding number, using number facts and calculating. In this book we have focused on the objectives where parental involvement will be most effective.

Each unit features an introductory page for teachers (*Teacher's Notes*), a letter for parents (*Help at Home Sheet*) that can be photocopied and sent home and two pupil worksheets (*Worksheets 1 and 2*). The calculation methods demonstrated on all the sheets are based on those recommended by the National Strategy.

Teacher's notes

These notes specify the learning objectives, learning outcomes and success criteria for each unit as well as suggesting opportunities for using and applying the skill being practised. The questions listed under 'Success criteria' are intended as prompts on which to base ongoing pupil assessment.

Help at home sheet

This is a letter for parents explaining what is being taught and, where appropriate, it also shows worked examples for parents to follow. There are also some ideas for relevant activities that can be completed at home. Introducing maths into everyday situations can increase a child's confidence and they can end up tackling complex number operations without even realising they are 'doing maths'.

Worksheets 1 and 2

The two worksheets provide activities that can be used by pupils for learning, for practising and for assessment. Where possible the children are encouraged to participate in their own assessment, identifying what they can do. Once a sheet is completed, discuss it with the child and help them to think about their own learning process. Ask questions such as 'How did you get on? Did you like this work? Did you find any of it too challenging?' With the second worksheet, discuss with the child whether they feel able to tick the 'I can' boxes. Celebrate their successes and support them if they are not ready to tick the boxes yet, by explaining that they will have another chance to revisit the concept and get more practice until they feel more confident.

Andrew Brodie: Number Journey for ages 5-6 © A&C Black Publishers Ltd 2008

Estimating and counting

Teacher's notes

Building on previous learning
Before starting this unit check that the children can already:
- say and use number names in order in familiar contexts
- know that numbers identify how many objects are in a set
- count reliably up to 10 everyday objects
- estimate how many objects they can see and check by counting
- count aloud in ones
- use ordinal numbers in different contexts
- recognise numerals 1 to 9

Learning objectives
- Count reliably at least 20 objects, recognising that when rearranged the number of objects stays the same.
- Estimate a number of objects that can be checked by counting.
- Write numerals from 0 to 20, then beyond.

Learning outcomes
- The children will be able to give sensible estimates for the number of objects presented to them or for the number of items shown in a picture.
- The children will have effective strategies for counting, such as moving objects from one pile to another or drawing a line through items in a picture as they are counted.
- The children will be able to write the numbers from 0 to 20 using correctly formed numerals.

Success criteria
Can the children...
- … estimate sensibly when you scatter in front of them the following numbers of counters, small bricks or beads: 3, 9, 14, 20, 23?
- … count successfully the following numbers of objects or items in pictures: 5, 8, 17, 24? (You could use Worksheet 2 for this assessment.)
- … write clearly the following numbers: 6, 12, 15, 19, 21, 25?

Resources needed
- A variety of counters, small bricks, beads, etc.

Opportunities for using and applying the skills

There are many occasions when counting can be used in everyday life such as:
- estimating then counting how many people are present today
- estimating then counting the number of people sitting around the table
- estimating then counting the number of pencils in the pencil pot – are there enough for the people sitting around the table?

Andrew Brodie: Number Journey for ages 5-6 © A&C Black Publishers Ltd 2008

Estimating and counting

Help at home sheet

Child's name: Kaitlin   **Date:** 15\VI\15

Dear Parents

At school we follow the National Curriculum and the Primary Framework for mathematics. One aspect of our work in mathematics is the learning of number skills and part of that is, of course, counting. We are keen to involve parents in their children's learning so you may like to help your child by using some of the ideas on this sheet.

National Curriculum

The Primary Framework for mathematics says that Year 1 pupils should:

- count reliably at least twenty objects, recognising that when rearranged the number of objects stays the same;
- estimate a number of objects that can be checked by counting;
- read and write numerals from 0 to 20, then beyond.

You could...

… ask your child to estimate then count numbers of objects, such as:

How many biscuits are in a packet?

How many apples are in the fruit bowl?

How many tins are in the cupboard?

How many plates are in a pile?

How many steps are on the stairs?

How many grapes are in the bunch?

… ask your child to write the numbers clearly and correctly.

0 1 2 3 4 5 6 7 8 9

You may like to let us know how your child gets on with these activities – if so please return this sheet with any comments on the back.

Pairs of numbers with a total of 10

Teacher's notes

Building on previous learning
Before starting this unit check that the children can already:
- find one more or one less than any given number
- count reliably up to 10 everyday objects
- select two groups of objects to make a given total of objects

Learning objectives
- Derive all pairs of numbers with a total of 10.
- Recall all pairs of numbers with a total of 10.
- Use the equals (=) sign.

Learning outcomes
The children will be able to:
- find the correct number of objects to add to a given number of objects to make a total of 10.
- recall the combinations of pairs of numbers that add together to make a total of 10.

Success criteria
Can the children...
... draw and name the correct number of items to add to 4, 5, 8 or 7 to make 10?
... recall the pairs of numbers that make a total of 10?
... use the equals sign to represent addition?

Resources needed
- A number line from 0 to 10
- A variety of objects for counting

Opportunities for using and applying the skills
- Solving problems involving counting and adding in the context of numbers or money.
- Describing a problem using numbers, practical materials and diagrams; using these to solve the problem and set the solution in the original context.
- Answering a question by selecting and using suitable equipment, and sorting information, shapes or objects; displaying results using tables and pictures.

Pairs of numbers with a total of 10

Help at home sheet

Child's name: **Date:**

Dear Parents

At school we follow the National Curriculum and the Primary Framework for mathematics. One aspect of our work in mathematics is the learning of number skills, including learning all pairs of numbers that add up to ten: 0 + 10, 1 + 9, 2 + 8, 3 + 7, 4 + 6, 5 + 5, 6 + 4, 7 + 3, 8 + 2, 9 + 1, 10 + 0. We are keen to involve parents in their children's learning so you may like to help your child by using some of the ideas on this sheet.

National Curriculum

The Primary Framework for mathematics says that Year 1 pupils should:
- derive and recall all pairs of numbers with a total of 10.

You could...

… play a learning game using 10 socks. Ask your child to make a row of 10 socks then to close his/her eyes. You then hide 7 socks and ask your child to open his/her eyes and count the socks. Ask how many more socks are needed to make 10, then help your child to count them out – make sure that you say out loud what has happened: "We had 3 socks. We counted out 7 more socks to make a total of 10. 3 add 7 makes 10."

… keep repeating the game, hiding a different number of socks each time. The most important aspect of each game is to talk to your child about the numbers, making sure that he/she looks at the socks to see exactly how many there are in each group, then says what he/she sees e.g. "There are 8 socks and here are 2 more and that makes 10 altogether."

… find other items that can be counted to make 10 e.g. apples, plates, books, teddies, building bricks, etc.

You may like to let us know how your child gets on with these activities – if so please return this sheet with any comments on the back.

Andrew Brodie: Number Journey for ages 5-6 © A&C Black Publishers Ltd 2008

Pairs of numbers with a total of 10

Worksheet 1

Name: _Kaighn_

Date: _5\4\15_

On this page I am going to find pairs of numbers that make 10.

Farmer Ash wants 10 sheep in each pen. How many more does he need in each pen? Draw the sheep. Write the number.

 He needs ⌐ 6 ¬ more in this pen.

 He needs ⌐ 5 ¬ more in this pen.

 He needs ⌐ 2 ¬ more in this pen.

 He needs ⌐ 3 ¬ more in this pen.

23

Andrew Brodie: Number Journey for ages 5-6 © A&C Black Publishers Ltd 2008

Pairs of numbers with a total of 10

Name: _____

Date: _____

Write all the ways of making 10 by adding 2 numbers.
Two have been done for you.

6+4=10

4+6=10

10

Write the missing numbers in the boxes.

6 + ☐ = 10   3 + ☐ = 10

8 + ☐ = 10   0 + ☐ = 10

5 + ☐ = 10   9 + ☐ = 10

I can...   I can find pairs of numbers that add up to 10.   ☐
      I can remember pairs of numbers that add up to 10.   ☐

Andrew Brodie: Number Journey for ages 5-6 © A&C Black Publishers Ltd 2008

Subtracting from 10

Teacher's notes

Building on previous learning
Before starting this unit check that the children can already:
- find one more or one less than any given number
- count reliably up to 10 everyday objects
- find all pairs of numbers with a total of 10

Learning objectives
- Derive the subtraction facts when subtracting from 10.
- Recall the subtraction facts when subtracting from 10.
- Use the equals (=) sign.

Learning outcomes

- The children will be able to find the correct answer when a specified number is subtracted from 10.
- The children will be able to recall the subtraction facts when numbers are subtracted from 10.

Success criteria
Can the children...
... derive the subtraction from 10 facts:
  10 – 1, 10 – 2, 10 – 3, 10 – 4, 10 – 5, 10 – 6, 10 – 7, 10 – 8, 10 – 9, 10 – 10?
... recall the subtraction from 10 facts?
... use the equals sign to represent subtraction?

Resources needed

- A number line from 0 to 10
- A variety of objects for counting
- Some pennies

Opportunities for using and applying the skills
- Solving problems involving counting and subtracting in the context of numbers or money, for example finding change from 10p.
- Describing a problem using numbers, practical materials and diagrams; using these to solve the problem and set the solution in the original context.
- Answering a question by selecting and using suitable equipment, and sorting information, shapes or objects; displaying results using tables and pictures.

Andrew Brodie: Improving Comprehension for ages 5-6 © A&C Black Publishers Ltd 2008

Subtracting from 10

Help at home sheet

Child's name: **Date:**

Dear Parents

At school we follow the National Curriculum and the Primary Framework for mathematics. One aspect of our work in mathematics is the learning of number skills, including learning the subtractions from 10: 10 – 1, 10 – 2, 10 – 3, 10 – 4, 10 – 5, 10 – 6, 10 – 7, 10 – 8, 10 – 9, 10 – 10. We are keen to involve parents in their children's learning so you may like to help your child by using some of the ideas on this sheet.

National Curriculum

The Primary Framework for mathematics says that Year 1 pupils should:

- derive and recall all pairs of numbers with a total of 10 and addition facts for totals to at least 5; work out the corresponding subtraction facts.

You could...

… play a learning game using 10 spoons. Ask your child to make a row of 10 spoons. Now put 4 spoons to one side and ask him/her to say how many they think are left before he/she counts them. If you do this lots of times he/she will get better at saying how many are left. Make sure that you say out loud what has happened: "We had 10 spoons. I took away 4 spoons and there were 6 spoons left. 10 take away 4 is 6."

… keep repeating the game, subtracting a different number of spoons each time. The most important aspect of each game is to talk to your child about the numbers, making sure that he/she looks at the spoons to see exactly that there are 10 to start with, that some have been taken away and that there are a certain number left. Encourage your child to describe what has happened, e.g. "There were 10 spoons and you took 9 away so now there's only 1 spoon. 10 take away 9 is 1."

… find other items to use for subtraction e.g. oranges, plastic bottles, cups, books, teddies, building bricks, etc.

You may like to let us know how your child gets on with these activities – if so please return this sheet with any comments on the back.

Subtracting from 10

Worksheet 1

Name: _____

Date: _____

On this page I am going to find change from 10 pence.

 I buy a sweet for 3 pence.   I have [ ] pence left.

 I buy a pencil for 9 pence.   I have [ ] pence left.

 I buy a badge for 6 pence.   I have [ ] pence left.

 I buy a sticker for 5 pence.   I have [ ] pence left.

 I buy a marble for 8 pence.   I have [ ] pence left.

 I buy a puppet for 10 pence.   I have [ ] pence left.

27

Subtracting from 10

Name: _____

Date: _____

Write the answers to these subtractions.

10-2 =

10-9 =

10-1 =

10-7 =

10-10 =

10-8 =

10-5 =

10-4 =

10-6 =

Write the answers. The first one has been done for you.

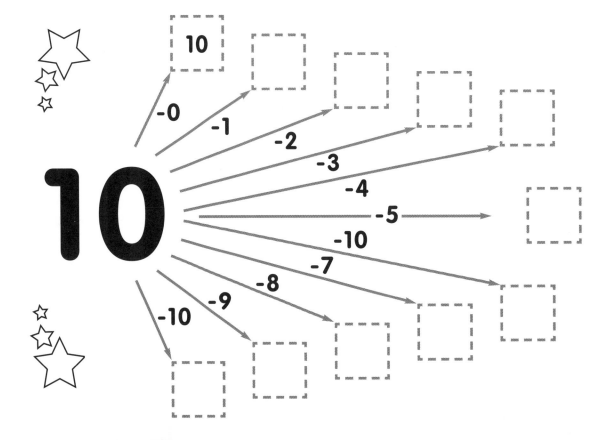

 I can find subtractions from 10. ☐

I can remember subtractions from 10. ☐

Andrew Brodie: Number Journey for ages 5-6 © A&C Black Publishers Ltd 2008

Addition facts for totals to at least 5

Teacher's notes

Building on previous learning
Before starting this unit check that the children can already:
- find one more or one less than any given number
- count reliably up to 10 everyday objects
- find all pairs of numbers with a total of 10

Learning objectives
- Derive the addition facts for totals to at least 5.
- Recall the addition facts for totals to at least 5.
- Use the equals (=) sign.

Learning outcomes
The children will be able to:
- find all combinations of pairs of numbers to make 2, 3, 4, 5, 6.
- recall the pairs of numbers that make 2, 3, 4 and 5.

Success criteria
Can the children...
... derive the addition to 5 facts: $4 + \boxed{} = 5$ $1 + \boxed{} = 5$ $3 + \boxed{} = 5$ $2 + \boxed{} = 5$
$5 + \boxed{} = 5$ $0 + \boxed{} = 5$
... recall the addition to 5 facts?
... derive the addition to 4 facts, the addition to 3 facts and the addition to 6 facts?
... recall the addition to 4 facts, the addition to 3 facts and the addition to 6 facts?

Resources needed
- A number line from 0 to 10
- A variety of objects for counting
- Some pennies

Opportunities for using and applying the skills
- Solving problems involving counting and adding in the context of numbers or money.
- Describing a problem using numbers, practical materials and diagrams; using these to solve the problem and set the solution in the original context.
- Answering a question by selecting and using suitable equipment, and sorting information, shapes or objects; displaying results using tables and pictures.

29

Addition facts for totals to at least 5

Help at home sheet

Child's name: Date:

Dear Parents

At school we follow the National Curriculum and the Primary Framework for mathematics. One aspect of our work in mathematics is the learning of number skills, including learning addition facts for totals to at least 5: e.g. $1 + 1 = 2$, $2 + 3 = 5$, etc. We are keen to involve parents in their children's learning so you may like to help your child by using some of the ideas on this sheet.

National Curriculum

The Primary Framework for mathematics says that Year 1 pupils should:

- derive and recall all pairs of numbers with a total of 10 and addition facts for totals to at least five; work out the corresponding subtraction facts.

You could...

… play a learning game using 5 building bricks. Ask your child to make a little tower of 5 bricks. Ask him/her to split the tower and to describe the 2 pieces that have been made. Encourage your child to say out loud what has happened: "The tower had 5 bricks and I split it into 2 pieces. This piece has 3 bricks and this piece has 2 bricks. 3 add 2 equals 5." Remind your child how this can be written down: $3 + 2 = 5$.

Ask him/her to put the 5 bricks back together as one tower and to split it in a different way. How many different ways can he/she find? Each time, encourage your child to talk about what he/she observes and to write it down if possible.

$$3 + 2 = 5$$

… do the same game using a tower of just 4 bricks. In some ways this is harder as there are less combinations to find: $3 + 1 = 4$, $2 + 2 = 4$, $1 + 3 = 4$. You could also discuss $0 + 4 = 4$

… find other items to use to make a set of five: bananas, plastic bottles, cups, books, teddies, etc.

… sing 'Five green bottles' or 'Five plastic bottles'.

You may like to let us know how your child gets on with these activities – if so please return this sheet with any comments on the back.

Andrew Brodie: Number Journey for ages 5-6 © A&C Black Publishers Ltd 2008

Addition facts for totals to at least 5

Worksheet 1

Name: _____

Date: _____

On this page I am going to find totals to 5 and to 4.

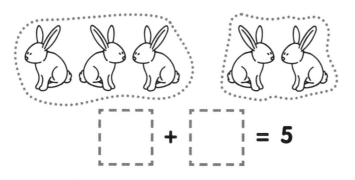 

☆   □ + □ = 5

Find other ways to split the rabbits into 2 groups.

□ + □ = 5

□ + □ = 5

□ + □ = 5

☆   □ + □ = 4

Find other ways to split the cats into 2 groups.

□ + □ = 4

□ + □ = 4

31

Andrew Brodie: Number Journey for ages 5-6 © A&C Black Publishers Ltd 2008

Addition facts for totals to at least 5

Worksheet 2

Name: _____

Date: _____

Write the missing numbers in the boxes.

4 + ☆ = 5   1 + ☆ = 5   3 + ☆ = 5

2 + ☆ = 5   5 + ☆ = 5   0 + ☆ = 5

Write the missing numbers in the boxes.

3 + ☆ = 4   1 + ☆ = 4   2 + ☆ = 4

Write the missing numbers in the boxes.

1 + ☆ = 3   2 + ☆ = 3   3 + ☆ = 3

Write the missing numbers in the boxes.

4 + ☆ = 6   2 + ☆ = 6   5 + ☆ = 6

I can...   I can find totals to 5. ☐
I can find totals to 6. ☐

Andrew Brodie: Number Journey for ages 5-6 © A&C Black Publishers Ltd 2008

Subtraction facts for numbers of 6 or fewer

Teacher's notes

Building on previous learning
Before starting this unit check that the children can already:
- find one more or one less than any given number
- count reliably up to 10 everyday objects
- find all pairs of numbers with a total of at least 5

Learning objectives
- Derive the subtraction facts for numbers of 6 or fewer.
- Recall the subtraction facts for numbers of 6 or fewer.
- Use the equals (=) sign.
- Understand subtraction as 'take away'.

Learning outcomes
The children will be able to:
- find all subtraction facts from 6, 5, 4, 3, 2 or 1.
- recall all subtraction facts from 5, 4, 3, 2 or 1.

Success criteria
Can the children…

… derive the facts for subtraction from 5 using the process of 'taking away':

$5 - 1 = \boxed{}$ $5 - 3 = \boxed{}$ $5 - 4 = \boxed{}$ $5 - 5 = \boxed{}$ $5 - 2 = \boxed{}$ $5 - 0 = \boxed{}$

… recall the subtraction from 5 facts?
… derive the subtraction from 4 facts, the subtraction from 3 facts and the subtraction from 6 facts?
… recall the subtraction from 4 facts, the subtraction from 3 facts and the subtraction from 6 facts?

Resources needed
- A number line from 0 to 10
- A variety of objects for counting
- Some pennies

Opportunities for using and applying the skills
- Solving problems involving counting and adding in the context of numbers or money.
- Describing a problem using numbers, practical materials and diagrams; using these to solve the problem and set the solution in the original context.
- Answering a question by selecting and using suitable equipment, and sorting information, shapes or objects; displaying results using tables and pictures.

Andrew Brodie: Number Journey for ages 5-6 © A&C Black Publishers Ltd 2008

Subtraction facts for numbers of 6 or fewer

Help at home sheet

Child's name: **Date:**

Dear Parents

At school we follow the National Curriculum and the Primary Framework for mathematics. One aspect of our work in mathematics is the learning of number skills, including learning subtraction facts from 5, 4, 3, 2 or 1. We are practising this using the process of 'taking away' rather than 'finding the difference', which we will look at on another occasion. We are keen to involve parents in their children's learning so you may like to help your child by using some of the ideas on this sheet.

National Curriculum

The Primary Framework for mathematics says that Year 1 pupils should:

- derive and recall all pairs of numbers with a total of 10 and addition facts for totals to at least 5; work out the corresponding subtraction facts;
- understand subtraction as 'take away' and find a 'difference'.

You could...

… play a learning game using 5 pound coins – it is very important only to use pound coins, not two-pound coins, fifty-pence pieces, etc. Say to your child: "Look, I've got 5 pound coins. If I go to the shop and I spend 2 pounds, how much have I got left?"

Your child may need to count the coins. Encourage him/her to describe what is happening: "You had 5 pounds. You spent 2 pounds. You've got 3 pounds left. 5 take away 2 is 3."

Now repeat the activity, this time 'spending' 4 pounds, or 3 pounds or 1 pound. Try spending 5 pounds so that your child can see there is nothing left.

… find other items to use. Small sweets such as chocolate buttons can be useful. "I've got 4 chocolate buttons. If I eat 3 of them how many will I have left?" Keep practising, praising your child when he/she is able to explain the subtraction. When he/she is finding it easy you could simply ask questions such as '5 take away 2', '4 take away 4', '3 subtract 1', etc.

You may like to let us know how your child gets on with these activities – if so please return this sheet with any comments on the back.

Andrew Brodie: Number Journey for ages 5-6 © A&C Black Publishers Ltd 2008

Subtraction facts for numbers of 6 or fewer

Worksheet 1

Name: _____

Date: _____

On this page I am going to find subtractions from numbers up to 6.

Sam has 5 apples. If he eats 3 of them, how many will he have left?

5 – 3 = ☐ ☆

Now try these.

5 – 2 = ☐ ☆   5 – 1 = ☐ ☆   5 – 4 = ☐ ☆

6 – 2 = ☐ ☆   6 – 5 = ☐ ☆   6 – 3 = ☐ ☆

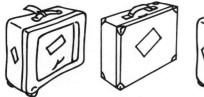

3 – 1 = ☐ ☆   3 – 3 = ☐ ☆   3 – 2 = ☐ ☆

Andrew Brodie: Number Journey for ages 5-6 © A&C Black Publishers Ltd 2008

Subtraction facts for numbers of 6 or fewer

Worksheet 2

Name: _____

Date: _____

Write the missing numbers in the boxes.

5 – 1 = ☐   5 – 3 = ☐   5 – 4 = ☐

5 – 5 = ☐   5 – 2 = ☐   5 – 0 = ☐

Write the missing numbers in the boxes.

4 – 2 = ☐   4 – 1 = ☐   4 – 3 = ☐

Write the missing numbers in the boxes.

6 – 3 = ☐   6 – 1 = ☐   6 – 4 = ☐

6 – 5 = ☐   6 – 2 = ☐   6 – 0 = ☐

Write the missing numbers in the boxes.

3 – 3 = ☐   3 – 1 = ☐   3 – 2 = ☐

I can... I can find subtractions from 3, 4, 5 and 6. ☐
I can remember subtractions from 3, 4, 5 and 6. ☐

36

Andrew Brodie: Number Journey for ages 5-6 © A&C Black Publishers Ltd 2008

Doubles of all numbers to at least 10

Teacher's notes

Building on previous learning
Before starting this unit check that the children can already:
- find one more or one less than any given number
- count reliably at least 20 objects
- read and write numerals from 0 to 20 and beyond

Learning objectives
- Derive the doubles of all numbers to at least 10.
- Recall the doubles of all numbers to at least 10.
- Use the equals (=) sign.

Learning outcomes
The children will be able to:
- find doubles of all numbers from 1 to 12.
- recall doubles of all numbers from 1 to 10.

Success criteria
Can the children…
… derive the doubles of numbers from 1 to 12?
… recall the doubles of 1, 2, 3, 4, 5, 6, 7, 8, 9, 10?

Resources needed
- A number line from 0 to 30
- A variety of objects for counting
- Dice

Opportunities for using and applying the skills
- Solving problems involving counting and doubling in the context of numbers or money.
- Describing a problem using numbers, practical materials and diagrams; using these to solve the problem and set the solution in the original context.
- Answering a question by selecting and using suitable equipment, and sorting information, shapes or objects; displaying results using tables and pictures.

Doubles of all numbers to at least 10

Help at home sheet

Child's name: **Date:**

Dear Parents

At school we follow the National Curriculum and the Primary Framework for mathematics. One aspect of our work in mathematics is the learning of number skills, including learning the doubles of 1, 2, 3, 4, 5, 6, 7, 8, 9 and 10. We are keen to involve parents in their children's learning so you may like to help your child by using some of the ideas on this sheet.

National Curriculum

The Primary Framework for mathematics says that Year 1 pupils should:

- recall the doubles of all numbers to at least 10.

You could...

… hold up the fingers of one hand and ask your child how many fingers he/she can see. Encourage him/her to say '5' rather than '4 fingers and 1 thumb'! Now hold up the other hand and ask how many fingers are on that hand. Now ask how many fingers are on both hands. Discuss the maths, ensuring that you say 'double 5 is 10'. Try just showing 4 fingers on one hand – ask your child to say how many there are then ask, 'what's double 4?' Keep practising with all the doubles to 5: 'double 1', 'double 2', 'double 3', 'double 4', 'double 5'.

…when your child is confident with the doubles to 5, try a matching hands game: Hold up 1 hand with 5 fingers held up clearly, and the other hand with 2 fingers shown clearly. Ask your child how many fingers you are holding up altogether, then ask him/her to match your hands with his/hers. Ask how many fingers are being held up altogether. Encourage your child to say, 'double 7 is 14'.

You may like to let us know how your child gets on with these activities – if so please return this sheet with any comments on the back.

Doubles of all numbers to at least 10

Worksheet 1

Name: _____

Date: _____

On this page I am going to find doubles of numbers.

There are 5 dots on each dice. Double 5 makes 10 altogether.

Double **5** = **10**

Find these doubles.

Double **6** = ☆

Double **2** = ☆

Double **4** = ☆

Double **3** = ☆

Double **1** = ☆

Here are 8 balls.

Draw 8 more balls.

Double **8** = ☆

Now try these.

Double **7** = ☆   Double **9** = ☆

Andrew Brodie: Number Journey for ages 5-6 © A&C Black Publishers Ltd 2008

Doubles of all numbers to at least 10

Worksheet 2

Name: _____

Date: _____

Write the missing numbers in the boxes.

Double **6** = ⬜ ☆

Double **8** = ⬜ ☆

Double **3** = ⬜ ☆

Double **4** = ⬜ ☆

Double **1** = ⬜ ☆

Double **5** = ⬜ ☆

Double **10** = ⬜ ☆

Double **2** = ⬜ ☆

Double **9** = ⬜ ☆

Double **7** = ⬜ ☆

Try these. You can draw pictures to help.

Double **11** = ⬜ ☆

Double **12** = ⬜ ☆

 I can...
I can find doubles of numbers up to 10. ⬜
I can remember doubles of numbers up to 10. ⬜
I can find doubles of 11 and 12. ⬜

40

Count on or back in twos

Teacher's notes

Building on previous learning
Before starting this unit check that the children can already:
- find one more or one less than any given number
- count reliably at least 20 objects
- read and write numerals from 0 to 20 and beyond

Learning objectives
- Count on in twos to 20.
- Count back in twos from 20.
- Derive the multiples of 2 to the 10th multiple.

Learning outcomes
The children will be able to:
- count in twos from 0 to 20.
- count in twos from 20 to 0.
- identify the multiples of 2 up to 10 x 2.

Success Criteria
Can the children…
… write the multiples of 2 from 0 to 20 in order?
… write the multiples of 2 from 20 to 0 in order?
… identify the multiples of 2 in relation to pictures of objects?

Resources needed
- A number line from 0 to 20
- A number track from 0 to 20

Opportunities for using and applying the skills
- Describing simple patterns and relationships involving numbers or shapes.
- Answering a question by selecting and using suitable equipment, and sorting information, shapes or objects; displaying results using tables and pictures.

Andrew Brodie: Number Journey for ages 5-6 © A&C Black Publishers Ltd 2008

Count on or back in twos

Help at home sheet

Child's name: **Date:**

Dear Parents

At school we follow the National Curriculum and the Primary Framework for mathematics. One aspect of our work in mathematics is the learning of number skills, including learning to count in twos – this will help the children when they start to learn the 2 times table. We are keen to involve parents in their children's learning so you may like to help your child by using some of the ideas on this sheet.

National Curriculum

The Primary Framework for mathematics says that Year 1 pupils should:

- count on or back in twos and use this knowledge to derive the multiples of 2 to the 10th multiple.

You could...

… use the socks again! Show your child 3 pairs of socks and ask him/her how many there are altogether. Count them in ones with your child: '1, 2, 3, 4, 5, 6.' Now count them in pairs together: '2, 4, 6.' Ensure that your child can see that there are 6 socks with both ways of counting. Now try a different number of pairs and ask your child to count in twos again. Keep practising, and praising every success.

 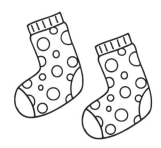 

… use a number line. Point to zero and explain to your child that you are going to miss out the next number and jump straight to 2, then miss the next number and jump to 4, then miss the next and jump to 6 – point to each number as you reach it and each time 'jump' your finger on to the next multiple of 2.

0 1 2 3 4 5 6 7 8 9 10 11 12

You may like to let us know how your child gets on with these activities – if so please return this sheet with any comments on the back.

Count on or back in twos

Name: _____

Date: _____

On this page I am going to count on in twos.
On this page I am going to count back in twos.

Look at the number track. Colour the boxes that have arrows.

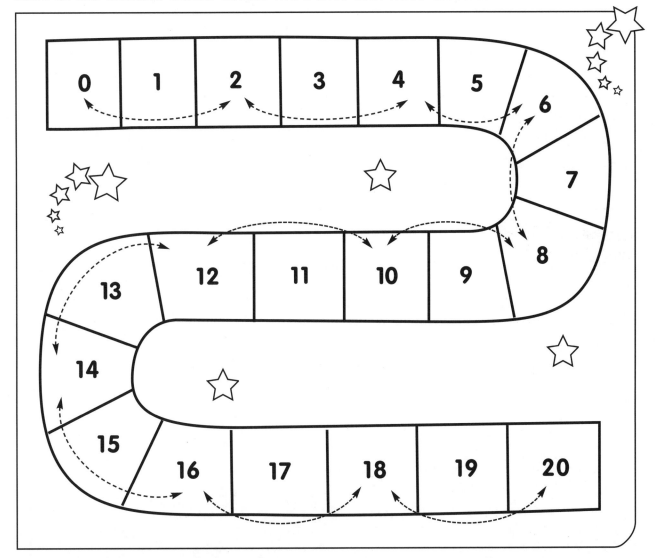

Write the numbers that you coloured.
Make sure you write them in the correct order.

> 2 | | | | | | | | | | |

Now write the numbers again but this time start at 20 and count back.

> 20 | | | | | | | | | |

Count on or back in twos

Name: _____

Date: _____

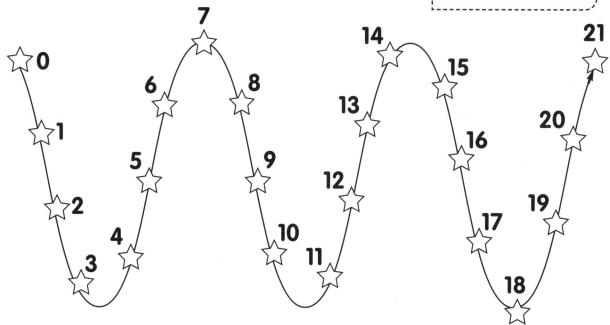

Count on in twos. The first three have been done for you.

0	2	4								

Count back in twos. The first three have been done for you.

20	18	16								

Write the correct number for each picture.

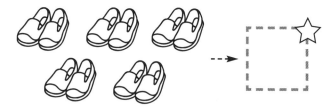

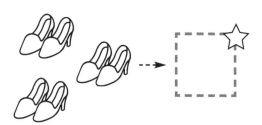

 I can...

I can count on in twos. ☐
I can count back in twos. ☐
I can find the multiples of 2. ☐

44

Andrew Brodie: Number Journey for ages 5-6 © A&C Black Publishers Ltd 2008

Count on or back in tens

Teacher's notes

Building on previous learning
Before starting this unit check that the children can already:
- find one more or one less than any given number
- find 10 more or 10 less than any multiple of 10
- count reliably at least 20 objects
- read and write numerals from 0 to 20 and beyond

Learning objectives
- Count on in tens to 100.
- Count back in tens from 100.
- Derive the multiples of 10 to the 10th multiple.

Learning outcomes

The children will be able to:
- count in tens from 0 to 100.
- count in tens from 100 to 0.
- identify the multiples of 10 up to 10 x 10.

Success Criteria
Can the children…
… write the multiples of 10 from 0 to 100 in order?
… write the multiples of 10 from 100 to 0 in order?
… identify the multiples of 10 in relation to pictures of objects?

Resources needed
- A number line from 0 to 100
- A number track from 0 to 100

Opportunities for using and applying the skills

- Describing simple patterns and relationships involving numbers or shapes.
- Answering a question by selecting and using suitable equipment, and sorting information, shapes or objects; displaying results using tables and pictures.
- Solve problems involving counting in the context of numbers or money.

Count on or back in tens

Help at home sheet

Child's name: **Date:**

Dear Parents

At school we follow the National Curriculum and the Primary Framework for mathematics. One aspect of our work in mathematics is the learning of number skills, including learning to count in tens – this will help the children when they start to learn the ten times table. We are keen to involve parents in their children's learning so you may like to help your child by using some of the ideas on this sheet.

National Curriculum

The Primary Framework for mathematics says that Year 1 pupils should:

- count on or back in tens and use this knowledge to derive the multiples of 10 to the 10th multiple.

You could...

… ask as many members of the family as possible to take their shoes and socks off! Sit together on the floor and count 10, 20, 30, etc, up to 100 – ensure that your child understands that you are counting 10 fingers then 10 toes each time. Keep practising, and praising every success.

… use a number line from 0 to 100. Point to zero and explain to your child that you are going to jump straight to 10, then jump to 20, etc – point to each number as you reach it and each time 'jump' your finger on to the next multiple of 10.

| 0 | 10 | 20 | 30 | 40 | 50 | 60 | 70 | 80 | 90 | 100 | 110 |

You may like to let us know how your child gets on with these activities – if so please return this sheet with any comments on the back.

Count on or back in tens

Name: _____

Date: _____

On this page I am going to count on in tens.
On this page I am going to count back in tens.

Write the correct numbers in the empty boxes.

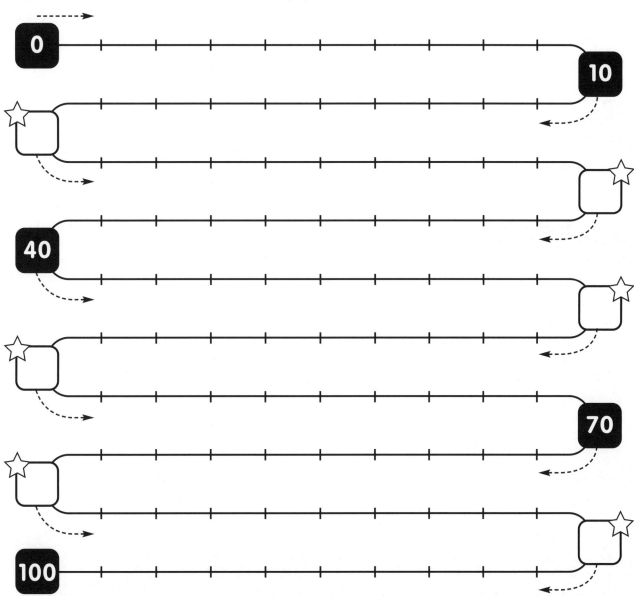

Write the numbers that are in the boxes. Make sure you write them in the correct order.

Now write the numbers again but this time start at 100 and count back.

100

Andrew Brodie: Number Journey for ages 5-6 © A&C Black Publishers Ltd 2008

Count on or back in tens

Worksheet 2

Name: _____

Date: _____

Count on in tens. The first 3 have been done for you.

0	10	20								

Count back in tens. The first 3 have been done for you.

100	90	80								

Write the correct number for each picture.

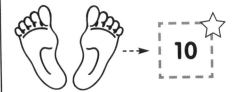 10

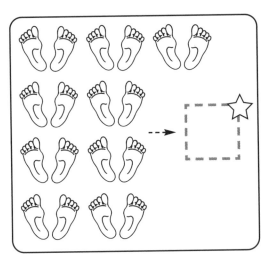

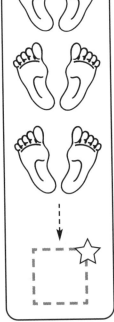

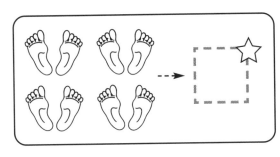

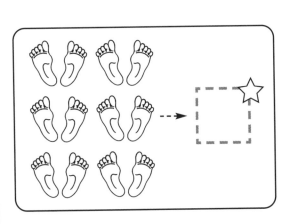

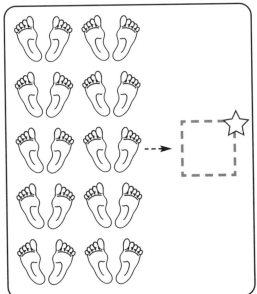

I can...
I can count on in tens. ☐
I can count back in tens. ☐
I can find the multiples of 10 ☐

48

Andrew Brodie: Number Journey for ages 5-6 © A&C Black Publishers Ltd 2008

Count on or back in fives

Teacher's notes

Building on previous learning
Before starting this unit check that the children can already:
- find one more or one less than any given number
- count reliably at least 20 objects
- read and write numerals from 0 to 20 and beyond
- compare and order numbers using the related vocabulary

Learning objectives
- Count on in fives to 50.
- Count back in fives from 50.
- Derive the multiples of 5 to the 10th multiple.

Learning outcomes
The children will be able to:
- count in fives from 0 to 50.
- count in fives from 50 to 0.
- identify the multiples of 5 up to 10 x 5.

Success criteria
Can the children…
… write the multiples of 5 from 0 to 50 in order?
… write the multiples of 5 from 50 to 0 in order?
… identify the multiples of 5 in relation to pictures of objects?

Resources needed
- A number line from 0 to 50
- A number track from 0 to 50

Opportunities for using and applying the skills
- Describing simple patterns and relationships involving numbers or shapes.
- Answering a question by selecting and using suitable equipment, and sorting information, shapes or objects; displaying results using tables and pictures.

49

Count on or back in fives

Help at home sheet

Dear Parents

At school we follow the National Curriculum and the Primary Framework for mathematics. One aspect of our work in mathematics is the learning of number skills, including learning to count in fives – this will help the children when they start to learn the 5 times table. We are keen to involve parents in their children's learning so you may like to help your child by using some of the ideas on this sheet.

National Curriculum

The Primary Framework for mathematics says that Year 1 pupils should:

- count on or back in fives and use this knowledge to derive the multiples of 5 to the 10th multiple.

You could...

… use everybody's hands. Make sure that your child can count 5 fingers on one person's hand and that he/she knows that all the hands have 5 fingers each. Stand in a ring and choose who starts: that person holds up 1 hand and says '5', then the other hand and says '10'; the next person holds up a hand and says '15', then the other and says '20'. Continue this around the ring until '50' is reached. Keep practising, and praising for success. After lots of practice, ask your child to say the numbers while everyone else shows their hands but keeps quiet. When your child is confident, start at 50 and count back in fives to zero.

… use a number line from 0 to 50. Point to zero and explain to your child that you are going to jump straight to 5, then jump to 10, etc. Point to each number as you reach it and each time 'jump' your finger on to the next multiple of 5.

You may like to let us know how your child gets on with these activities – if so please return this sheet with any comments on the back.

Count on or back in fives

Worksheet 1

Name: _____

Date: _____

On this page I am going to count on in fives.
On this page I am going to count back in fives.

Look at the number track. Colour the 5, then count on 5 places and colour the 10. Keep counting on 5 places and colour the numbers you reach each time.

1	2	3	4	5	6	7	8	9	10
11	12	13	14	15	16	17	18	19	20
21	22	23	24	25	26	27	28	29	30
31	32	33	34	35	36	37	38	39	40
41	42	43	44	45	46	47	48	49	50

Write the numbers that you coloured. Make sure you write them in the correct order.

5

Now write the numbers again but this time start at 50 and count back.

50

Andrew Brodie: Number Journey for ages 5-6 © A&C Black Publishers Ltd 2008

Count on or back in fives

Name: _____

Date: _____

```
0    5   10   15   20   25   30   35   40   45   50   55
```

Count on in fives. The first 3 have been done for you.

| 0 | 5 | 10 | | | | | | | | | ☆ |

Count back in fives. The first 3 have been done for you.

| 50 | 45 | 40 | | | | | | | | | ☆ |

Write the correct number for each picture.

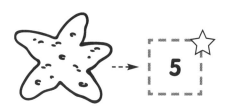 → 5

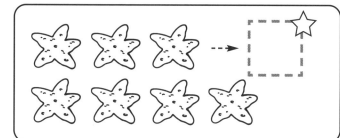

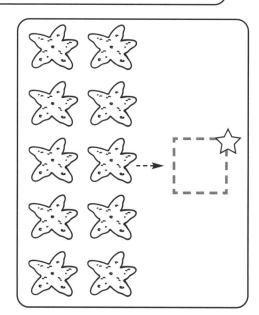

 I can...

I can count on in fives. ☐

I can count back in fives. ☐

I can find the multiples of 5 ☐

Andrew Brodie: Number Journey for ages 5-6 © A&C Black Publishers Ltd 2008

Addition by counting on

Teacher's notes

Building on previous learning
Before starting this unit check that the children can already:
- find one more or one less than any given number
- count reliably at least 20 objects
- read and write numerals from 0 to 20 and beyond
- compare and order numbers using the related vocabulary

Learning objectives

- Relate addition to counting on.
- Recognise that addition can be done in any order.
- Use practical and informal written methods to support the addition of a one-digit number to a one-digit or two-digit number.
- Use the equals sign.
- Use the vocabulary related to addition and symbols to describe and record addition number sentences.

Learning outcomes
The children will be able to:
- count on to solve an addition question.
- rearrange the numbers in a question to make the counting on operation easier.
- use appropriate vocabulary to describe addition number sentences.
- use appropriate symbols to record addition number sentences.

Success criteria
Can the children…
- … count on to find answers to questions such as 4 + 19, 7 + 26, 5 + 37, 6 + 42?
- … make decisions regarding which number to start from when answering questions such as 8 + 23, 15 + 6, 9 + 19, 17 + 5?
- … talk about the addition process for the above questions, using the appropriate vocabulary?
- … use the appropriate symbols correctly when finding the answers to the above questions?

Resources needed

- A number line from 0 to 50
- A number track from 0 to 50
- Counters

Opportunities for using and applying the skills
- Describing simple patterns and relationships involving numbers or shapes.
- Solving problems involving counting and adding in the context of numbers or money.

53

Addition by counting on

Help at home sheet

Child's name: Date:

Dear Parents

At school we follow the National Curriculum and the Primary Framework for mathematics. One aspect of our work in mathematics is the learning of number skills, including learning to add by counting on. We are keen to involve parents in their children's learning so you may like to help your child by using some of the ideas on this sheet.

National Curriculum

The Primary Framework for mathematics says that Year 1 pupils should:

- relate addition to counting on;
- recognise that addition can be done in any order;
- use practical and informal written methods to support the addition of a one-digit number to a one-digit or two-digit number.

You could...

… use real objects about the home, such as books or CD cases. Ask your child to count a pile of CD cases (make the pile less than 20). Now give him/her another pile (this time with less than 10) and ask him/her how many there are altogether. Encourage him/her to start from the number that he/she had previously counted e.g. if there were 18 CD cases in the first pile and 7 in the second pile, start by putting your hand on the pile of 18 and say '18' then count with your child by moving the extra 7 CD cases one at a time and saying '19', '20', etc until you reach the total of 25. When he/she can see how to do it, start with a different number and add another pile of CD cases. Encourage your child to count out loud.

0	5	10	15	20	25	30	35	40	45	50

1 2 3 4   6 7 8 9   11 12 13 14   16 17 18 19   21 22 23 24   26 27 28 29   31 32 33 34   36 37 38 39   41 42 43 44   46 47 48 49

…use a number line from 0 to 50. Point to a number and ask your child to add 6 to it; point to another number and ask your child to add 9; etc.

You may like to let us know how your child gets on with these activities – if so please return this sheet with any comments on the back.

Andrew Brodie: Number Journey for ages 5-6 © A&C Black Publishers Ltd 2008

Addition by counting on

Worksheet 1

Name: _____

Date: _____

On this page I am going to add by counting on.

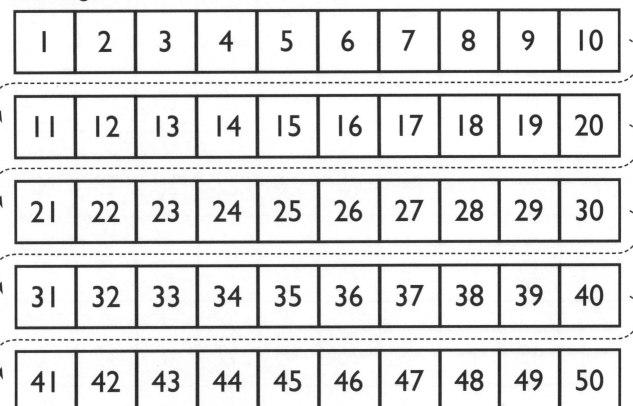

| 1 | 2 | 3 | 4 | 5 | 6 | 7 | 8 | 9 | 10 |

| 11 | 12 | 13 | 14 | 15 | 16 | 17 | 18 | 19 | 20 |

| 21 | 22 | 23 | 24 | 25 | 26 | 27 | 28 | 29 | 30 |

| 31 | 32 | 33 | 34 | 35 | 36 | 37 | 38 | 39 | 40 |

| 41 | 42 | 43 | 44 | 45 | 46 | 47 | 48 | 49 | 50 |

Start at 23. Count on 5 places.
What number do you land on?

$23 + 5 =$

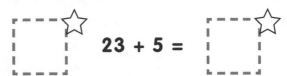

Use the number track to help you to answer these questions.

$31 + 6 =$ $12 + 7 =$

$9 + 3 =$ $28 + 5 =$

$19 + 8 =$ $7 + 5 =$

$38 + 4 =$ $41 + 9 =$

Andrew Brodie: Number Journey for ages 5-6 © A&C Black Publishers Ltd 2008

Addition by counting on

Worksheet 2

Name: _____

Date: _____

| 1 | 2 | 3 | 4 | 5 | 6 | 7 | 8 | 9 | 10 |

| 11 | 12 | 13 | 14 | 15 | 16 | 17 | 18 | 19 | 20 |

| 21 | 22 | 23 | 24 | 25 | 26 | 27 | 28 | 29 | 30 |

| 31 | 32 | 33 | 34 | 35 | 36 | 37 | 38 | 39 | 40 |

| 41 | 42 | 43 | 44 | 45 | 46 | 47 | 48 | 49 | 50 |

Use the number track to help you to answer these questions.
Start from the bigger number and add on the smaller number.

$4 + 19 =$ ☐ $7 + 26 =$ ☐

$5 + 37 =$ ☐ $6 + 42 =$ ☐

$8 + 23 =$ ☐ $15 + 6 =$ ☐

$9 + 19 =$ ☐ $17 + 5 =$ ☐

 I can...   I can add by counting on. ☐
I can decide which number to start on when adding. ☐

Andrew Brodie: Number Journey for ages 5-6 © A&C Black Publishers Ltd 2008

Subtraction: finding the difference by counting up

Teacher's notes

Building on previous learning
Before starting this unit check that the children can already:
- find one more or one less than any given number
- count reliably at least 20 objects
- read and write numerals from 0 to 20 and beyond
- compare and order numbers using the related vocabulary

Learning objectives
- Understand subtraction as finding a difference by counting up.
- Use practical and informal written methods to support the subtraction of a one-digit number from a one-digit or two-digit number.
- Use the equals sign.
- Use the vocabulary related to subtraction and symbols to describe and record subtraction number sentences.

Learning outcomes
The children will be able to:
- count on to solve a subtraction question.
- use appropriate vocabulary to describe subtraction number sentences.
- use appropriate symbols to record subtraction number sentences.

Success criteria
Can the children…
- … count up from the smaller number to find the difference in questions such as 24 – 19, 34 – 27, 42 – 39, 31 – 24, 13 – 8, 45 – 38, 26 – 18 and 38 – 29?
- … talk about the subtraction process for the above questions, using the appropriate vocabulary?
- … use the appropriate symbols correctly when finding the answers to the above questions?

Resources needed
- A number line from 0 to 50
- A number track from 0 to 50
- Counters

Opportunities for using and applying the skills
- Describing simple patterns and relationships involving numbers or shapes.
- Solving problems involving counting and subtracting in the context of numbers or money.

Andrew Brodie: Number Journey for ages 5-6 © A&C Black Publishers Ltd 2008

Subtraction: finding the difference by counting up

Help at home sheet

Child's name: **Date:**

Dear Parents

At school we follow the National Curriculum and the Primary Framework for mathematics. One aspect of our work in mathematics is the learning of number skills, including learning subtraction in the form of finding a difference by counting on. We are keen to involve parents in their children's learning so you may like to help your child by using some of the ideas on this sheet.

National Curriculum

The Primary Framework for mathematics says that Year 1 pupils should:

- understand subtraction as 'take away' and find a 'difference' by counting up;
- use practical and informal written methods to support the subtraction of a one-digit number from a one-digit or two-digit number.

You could...

… use real objects about the home, such as teaspoons and dessert spoons. Put 5 teaspoons and 8 dessert spoons on the table. Ask your child questions such as: "How many teaspoons are there?" "How many dessert spoons are there?" "How many more dessert spoons than teaspoons are there?" "What's the difference between five and eight?" Now practise this with other numbers of spoons or of different objects, giving your child lots of praise for success.

… use a number line from 0 to 50. Point to the number 11 and then to the number 17. Ask: "What's the difference between 11 and 17?" Encourage your child to start at the number 11 then to point to 12 and say '1', to point to 13 and say '2', etc until he/she reaches 17 and says '6'. Reinforce the answer by saying, "The difference between 11 and 17 is 6." Now point to 34 and then to 26. Ask: "What's the difference between 34 and 26?" Note that this time you have said the larger number first, but you should again encourage your child to start at the smaller number and count up. Keep working on lots of examples, helping your child where necessary and providing lots of praise for success.

You may like to let us know how your child gets on with these activities – if so please return this sheet with any comments on the back.

Subtraction: finding the difference by counting on

Worksheet 1

Name: _____

Date: _____

On this page I am going to find the
difference by counting up.

0 1 2 3 4 5 6 7 8 9 10 11 12 13 14 15 16 17 18 19 20

What is the difference between 13 and 8? Start on 8 and count up to 13.

How many steps do you take?

so $13 - 8 =$ [ ]

Use the number line to help you to answer these questions.

What is the difference between 6 and 14? $14 - 6 =$ [ ]

What is the difference between 15 and 8? $15 - 8 =$ [ ]

What is the difference between 12 and 4? $12 - 4 =$ [ ]

What is the difference between 9 and 13? $13 - 9 =$ [ ]

What is the difference between 5 and 11? $11 - 5 =$ [ ]

What is the difference between 13 and 8? $13 - 8 =$ [ ]

What is the difference between 7 and 15? $15 - 7 =$ [ ]

What is the difference between 9 and 17? $17 - 9 =$ [ ]

59

Andrew Brodie: Number Journey for ages 5-6 © A&C Black Publishers Ltd 2008

Subtraction: finding the difference by counting up

Worksheet 2

Name: _____

Date: _____

1	2	3	4	5	6	7	8	9	10

11	12	13	14	15	16	17	18	19	20

21	22	23	24	25	26	27	28	29	30

31	32	33	34	35	36	37	38	39	40

41	42	43	44	45	46	47	48	49	50

Use the number track to help you to answer these questions.

Find the difference between the 2 numbers.

Start from the smaller number and count up to the bigger number.

24 - 19 = ☐   34 - 27 = ☐

42 - 39 = ☐   31 - 24 = ☐

13 - 8 = ☐   45 - 38 = ☐

26 - 18 = ☐   38 - 29 = ☐

I can... I can find the difference by counting up. ☐

60

Andrew Brodie: Number Journey for ages 5-6 © A&C Black Publishers Ltd 2008

Adding a multiple of 10 by counting on

Teacher's notes

Building on previous learning
Before starting this unit check that the children can already:
- find one more or one less than any given number
- count reliably at least twenty objects
- read and write numerals from 0 to 20 and beyond
- compare and order numbers using the related vocabulary

Learning objectives
- Relate addition to counting on.
- Use practical and informal written methods to support the addition of a multiple of ten to a one-digit or two-digit number.
- Use the equals sign.
- Use the vocabulary related to addition and symbols to describe and record addition number sentences.

Learning outcomes
The children will be able to:
- count on to solve an addition question involving a multiple of ten.
- rearrange the numbers in a question to make the counting on operation easier.
- use appropriate vocabulary to describe addition number sentences.
- use appropriate symbols to record addition number sentence.

Success criteria
Can the children…
… find answers to questions such as 51 + 10, 63 + 20, 47 + 30, 20 + 37, 48 + 40, 50 + 13? make decisions regarding which number to start from when answering questions such as 50 + 13?
… talk about the addition process for the above questions, using the appropriate vocabulary?
… use the appropriate symbols correctly when finding the answers to the above questions?

Resources needed
- A hundred square. Note that some children find these confusing as the numbers go 'up' as you go 'down' the page. Correct use of language can help overcome this problem.
- Counters

Opportunities for using and applying the skills
- Describing simple patterns and relationships involving numbers or shapes.
- Solving problems involving counting and adding in the context of numbers or money.

Adding a multiple of 10 by counting on

Help at home sheet

Child's name: **Date:**

Dear Parents

At school we follow the National Curriculum and the Primary Framework for mathematics. One aspect of our work in mathematics is the learning of number skills, including learning to add a multiple of ten to a one-digit or two-digit number. We are keen to involve parents in their children's learning so you may like to help your child by using some of the ideas on this sheet.

National Curriculum

The Primary Framework for mathematics says that Year 1 pupils should:

- relate addition to counting on;
- recognise that addition can be done in any order;
- use practical and informal written methods to support the addition of a multiple of ten to a one-digit or two-digit number.

You could...

… use this number track to play a learning game. Ask your child to pick a number less than 40. Now ask him/her to add 10. Allow your child to count on to find the answer, by starting on the chosen number then pointing at the next number and saying '1', etc., until he/she reaches '10'. The number reached gives the answer to the question. After some practice with similar questions your child may realise that the answer can be found simply by jumping straight to the number that is written underneath the start number. This will help your child to get used to how a hundred square is laid out. Tell your child that he/she can have 10 points for every correct answer. Keep a record of his/her score and perhaps give a reward when he/she reaches 100. He/she will need to use his/her knowledge of numbers beyond 50 to keep the score correctly.

1	2	3	4	5	6	7	8	9	10
11	12	13	14	15	16	17	18	19	20
21	22	23	24	25	26	27	28	29	30
31	32	33	34	35	36	37	38	39	40
41	42	43	44	45	46	47	48	49	50

You may like to let us know how your child gets on with these activities – if so please return this sheet with any comments on the back.

Andrew Brodie: Number Journey for ages 5-6 © A&C Black Publishers Ltd 2008

Adding a multiple of 10 by counting on

Worksheet 1

Name: _____

Date: _____

On this page I am going to add 10 to other numbers.

Look at the hundred square.

1	2	3	4	5	6	7	8	9	10
11	12	13	14	15	16	17	18	19	20
21	22	23	24	25	26	27	28	29	30
31	32	33	34	35	36	37	38	39	40
41	42	43	44	45	46	47	48	49	50
51	52	53	54	55	56	57	58	59	60
61	62	63	64	65	66	67	68	69	70
71	72	73	74	75	76	77	78	79	80
81	82	83	84	85	86	87	88	89	90
91	92	93	94	95	96	97	98	99	100

Use the hundred square to help you to answer these questions. For each question start on the number that is 'not 10' then add the 10.

$31 + 10 = $

$53 + 10 = $

$17 + 10 = $

$10 + 49 = $

$68 + 10 = $

$10 + 72 = $

Adding a multiple of 10 by counting on

Worksheet 2

Name: _____

Date: _____

Look at the hundred square.

1	2	3	4	5	6	7	8	9	10
11	12	13	14	15	16	17	18	19	20
21	22	23	24	25	26	27	28	29	30
31	32	33	34	35	36	37	38	39	40
41	42	43	44	45	46	47	48	49	50
51	52	53	54	55	56	57	58	59	60
61	62	63	64	65	66	67	68	69	70
71	72	73	74	75	76	77	78	79	80
81	82	83	84	85	86	87	88	89	90
91	92	93	94	95	96	97	98	99	100

Use the hundred square to help you to answer these questions.

$51 + 10 =$

$63 + 20 =$

$47 + 30 =$

$20 + 37 =$

$48 + 40 =$

$50 + 13 =$

I can...

I can add 10 to other numbers.   ☐

I can add a multiple of 10 to other numbers.   ☐

64

Andrew Brodie: Number Journey for ages 5-6 © A&C Black Publishers Ltd 2008